CIRIA C625

Model agreements for sustainable water management systems

Model agreements for SUDS

P Shaffer   CIRIA

C Elliott   CIRIA

J Reed   Atkins

J Holmes   Weightman Vizards

M Ward   Atkins

CIRIA *sharing knowledge ■ building best practice*

Classic House, 174–180 Old Street, London EC1V 9BP
TEL +44 (0)20 7549 3300 FAX +44 (0)20 7253 0523
EMAIL enquiries@ciria.org
WEBSITE www.ciria.org

Summary

This guide provides basic advice on the use and development of model operation and maintenance agreements for SUDS alongside simple guidance on their incorporation in developments. It identifies maintenance considerations and provides an outline of how the long-term responsibilities for SUDS maintenance can be allocated.

Model agreements for sustainable water management systems. Model agreements for SUDS

CIRIA

Shaffer, P; Elliott, C; Reed, J; Holmes, J; Ward, M

CIRIA C625   © CIRIA 2004   ISBN 0-86017-625-8   RP664

Environment Agency Technical Report P2-261/19/TR1

British Library Cataloguing in Publication Data

A catalogue record is available for this book from the British Library.

Keywords		
Environmental good practice, pollution prevention, sustainable construction, urban drainage, urban hydrogeology, water quality		
Reader interest	**Classification**	
Developers, landscape architects, consulting engineers, local authorities, architects, highway authorities, environmental regulators, planners, sewerage undertakers, contractors, property-owners and other organisations involved in the provision or maintenance of surface water drainage to new and existing developments	AVAILABILITY	Unrestricted
	CONTENT	Technical guidance and model agreement
	STATUS	Committee-guided
	USER	Developers, architects, engineers, regulators

Published by CIRIA, Classic House, 174–180 Old Street, London EC1V 9BP, UK.

Background to the guide

This guide has been prepared for use by all organisations involved in the provision and maintenance of sustainable water management systems. This may include:

- owners and developers
- landscape architects
- consulting engineers
- land use planners
- architects
- environmental regulators
- sewerage undertakers
- residents
- tenants
- facility managers
- property and landowners.

Model agreements for sustainable water management systems is a series of documents resulting from a research project undertaken by CIRIA to facilitate and encourage the long-term maintenance of sustainable drainage systems (SUDS) and rainwater/ greywater use systems through the development and application of model agreements. A model agreement is just one method of allocating responsibilities for the maintenance of systems and consists of a legal agreement that can be used as the basis for agreements between two or more parties.

There are two main outputs to the series.

Model agreements for SUDS. This document provides background and a long-term framework for the operation and maintenance of SUDS. Model agreements were developed for specific scenarios:

- implementation and maintenance of SUDS through the planning process, either as a planning obligation under Section 106 of the Town and Country Planning Act 1990 or as a condition attached to planning permission
- implementation and maintenance of SUDS between two or more parties (outside of the requirements for planning permission), ie private SUDS model agreement

Model agreements for rainwater/greywater use systems. This sister document provides background to the operation and maintenance of rainwater/greywater use systems, providing a framework for the long-term operation and maintenance of reuse systems. The model agreement is set out for a variety of scenarios, ranging from single properties to multi-occupancy properties.

The documents in this series are not intended for use as extensive reference documentation on the design and implementation of sustainable water management systems but are designed to complement existing guidance documents and frameworks. Full details of such guidance are given in Chapter 1.

Acknowledgements

Research contractor

This guidance document is the outcome of Research Project 664. It was prepared by **CIRIA** and **Atkins** and **Weightman Vizards**.

Authors

Paul Shaffer, BSc
Paul is a project manager with CIRIA and for eight years has encouraged and implemented the sustainable use and management of water in the built environment. He is responsible for a number of projects designed to help overcome the perceived technical and management barriers to the sustainable management of water.

Craig Elliott, BA, MSc
Craig is an associate at CIRIA with responsibility for CIRIA's work in the water and utilities market area. He has more than 16 years' experience of research into water and environmental issues, particularly into water sustainability, surface water management and linking hydrology and ecology.

Jon Reed, BSc, MSc, CEng, MICE, MCIWEM
Jonathan is a chartered civil and environmental engineer whose experience spans water resources, sustainable development and infrastructure design. He is responsible for feasibility and design work for SUDS solutions for both new-build and retrofit situations. He has also represented developers and local authorities with respect to the implementation of SUDS through the planning process.

John Holmes, BA, LLB
John is a partner at Weightman Vizards Solicitors where he is head of Commercial Property, Planning, Environmental and Construction. Based in Manchester and an acknowledged specialist in his field, he has long experience of the public sector. This expertise extends to advising on all aspects of planning and environmental law.

Martin Ward, BEng, MSc, MPhil, CEng, MIMechE
Martin is a chartered mechanical engineer with more than 10 years' experience of the water industry. He spent eight years in Anglian Water's Research and Development Department, where he researched new water treatment and recycling processes and was involved in the practical application of rainwater, greywater and blackwater recycling projects. Currently, he is a project manager with Atkins Ltd, working mainly on the renovation and design of sewage treatment works.

Steering group

Following CIRIA's usual practice, the research project was guided by a steering group, as listed below.

Chair	Charles Ainger	MWH
Attending members	David Barraclough	Royal Town Planning Institute
	Nick Cooper	Atlantis Water Management Ltd
	Rupert Cowen	Hammond Suddards Edge
	Mark Everard	The Natural Step/Environment Agency
	Ian Hardwick	JJ Gallagher
	Paul Jeffrey	Cranfield University
	Denis Lane	Stevenage Borough Council
	Rebecca Lemon/	
	David Calderbank	Environment Agency
	Lawrence Mbugua	Davis Langdon Consultancy (DTI representative)
	Alex Middleton	The Greenbelt Group of Companies Ltd

Terry Nash	Gusto Construction Ltd
John Nicholson	Severn Trent Water
Stan Redfearn	The BOC Foundation
Andrew Shuttleworth	SEL Environmental
Neil Smith	NHBC
Chris Tyler	WSP Development Ltd
Tom Wild	SEPA
Steve Wilson	Environmental Protection Group Ltd

Corresponding members

Nick Beckwith/Marc Haley	Wardell Armstrong
Philip Day	Severn Trent Water Ltd
Steve Dickie	Entec Ltd
Richard Kellagher	HR Wallingford Ltd
Robin Mynard	DEFRA
Simon Walster	Ofwat

CIRIA managers

CIRIA's research managers for the project were **Paul Shaffer** and **Craig Elliott**.

Project funders

The project was funded by:

CIRIA Core Programme
Department of Trade and Industry
The BOC Foundation
Environment Agency
Severn Trent Water
Ofwat
NHBC
WSP Development
SEL Environmental
Environmental Protection Group Ltd

Contributors

CIRIA and the research contractors wish to acknowledge the following individuals who provided information, help and feedback for the project and whose contributions have been important to the development of the model agreements:

Ken Banfield	Anglian Water
Bob Bray	Robert Bray Associates
Reg Brown	BSRIA
Dave Brook	ODPM – Planning
David Butler	Imperial College
Jim Conlin	Scottish Water
Denis Cooper	Ipswich Borough Council
Robert Cunningham	The Wildlfe Trusts
Graham Fairhurst	Borough of Telford & Wrekin
David Gallagher	Environment Agency (greywater trialist)
Carolin Gohler	Cambridge City Council
Nick Grant	Elemental Solutions
Gill Greatorex	Environment Agency (greywater trialist)
Cath Hassell	Construction Resources
John Hamilton	Northern Ireland Water Service
David Harley	SEPA
Andy Hawkes	JJ Gallagher
Sian Hills	Thames Water
Mark Holland	SANDS
Brian Hurst	Freewater UK
Kendrick Jackson	formerly Gleeson Homes, now House Builders Federation

Chris Jefferies	University of Abertay
Phil Jobson	Welcome Break
Peter Johns	Formpave
Mike Johnson	ODPM
Bruce Kavanagh	Tully D'Ath
Chris Kearns	South Gloucestershire Council
David Knaggs	Metropolitan Water Company
Denis Lane	Stevenage Borough Council
Richard Lemon	Hampshire CC
Kevin Light	Davies Light Associates
Kirsteen Macdonald	Ewan Associates
Chris Mackenzie	Harborough District Council
Prosper Paul	Environment Agency
Stella Peterson	Salford City Council
Neil Robinson-Welsh	Drainage Management
Owen Saward	Wealden District Council
David Sellers	Leeds City Council
Chris Shirley-Smith	Water Works UK
Nick Trollope	Fairview New Homes
Mike Waite	DEFRA
Adrian Watkins	CEIMA Ltd
Joe Whiteman	Countryside Properties
Paul Williams	Gramm Environmental
Peter Woods	Tesco

Other contributors CIRIA and the research contractors would also like to acknowledge the following organisations for their help in preparing the model agreements:

National SUDS Working Group
UK Rainwater Harvesting Association

Contents

Figures and tables

FIGURES

TABLES

Glossary

Attenuation – To reduce the peak flow and increase the duration of a flow event.

Balancing pond – A pond designed to attenuate flows by storing runoff during the peak flow and releasing it at a controlled rate during and after the storm. Also known as wet detention pond.

Basin – A ground depression acting as a flow control or water treatment structure that normally is dry and has a proper outfall, but which is designed to detain stormwater temporarily.

Catchment – The area contributing surface water flow to a point on a drainage or river system. Can be divided into sub-catchments.

Combined sewer – A sewer designed to carry foul sewage and surface runoff in the same pipe.

Commuted sum – A single payment made at the beginning of an agreement to cover maintenance for an agreed period of time.

CSO (combined sewer overflow) – An outfall from a combined sewer designed to prevent the capacity of sewage treatment works from being exceeded under storm flow conditions by allowing the discharge of excess diluted sewage to a watercourse.

Curtilage – Land area within property boundaries.

Design criteria – A set of standards agreed by the developer, planners and regulators that the proposed system should satisfy.

Detention basin – A vegetated depression that normally is dry except following storm events. It is constructed to store water temporarily to attenuate flows and may allow infiltration of water to the ground.

Environmental regulators – The Environment Agency in England and Wales, SEPA in Scotland, and the Northern Ireland Environment and Heritage Service in Northern Ireland.

Extended detention basin – A detention basin where the runoff is stored beyond the time for attenuation. This provides extra time for natural processes to remove some of the pollutants in the water.

Filter drain or filter trench – A linear drain consisting of a trench filled with a permeable material, often with a perforated pipe in the base of the trench to assist drainage. Its purpose is to store and conduct water, but may also permit infiltration.

Filter strip – A vegetated area of gently sloping ground designed to drain water evenly off impermeable areas and filter out silt and other particulates.

Filtration – The act of removing sediment or other particles from a fluid by passing it through a filter.

First flush – The initial runoff from a site/catchment following the start of a rainfall event. As runoff travels over a catchment it will collect or dissolve pollutants and the "first flush" portion of the flow may be the most contaminated as a result. This is especially the case for intense storms and in small or more uniform catchments. In larger or more complex catchments pollution wash-off may contaminate runoff throughout a rainfall event.

Flow control device – A device used to manage the movement of surface water into and out of an attenuation facility, eg weirs.

Greywater – Greywater is wastewater from sinks, baths, showers and domestic appliances. Kitchen sink or dishwasher wastewater is not generally collected for use, as it has high levels of contamination from detergents, fats and food waste, making filtering and treatment difficult and costly.

Highways Agency – The UK Government agency responsible for strategic highways.

Highway authority – A local authority with responsibility for the maintenance and drainage of highways maintainable at public expense.

Impermeable surface – An artificial non-porous surface that generates a surface water runoff after rainfall.

Infiltration (to the ground) – The passage of surface water through the surface of the ground.

Infiltration basin – A dry basin designed to promote infiltration of surface water to the ground.

Infiltration trench – A trench, usually filled with permeable granular material, designed to promote infiltration of surface water to the ground.

Model Agreement – A legal document that can be completed to form the basis of an agreement between two or more parties regarding the maintenance and operation of sustainable water management systems.

Permeable surface – A surface that is formed of material that is itself impervious to water but, by virtue of voids formed through the surface, allows infiltration of water to the sub-base – for example, concrete block paving.

Pervious surface – A surface that allows inflow of rainwater into the underlying construction or soil.

Pond – Permanently wet depression designed to retain stormwater above the permanent pool and permit settlement of suspended solids and biological removal of pollutants.

Rainwater use systems – A system that collects rainwater from where it falls rather than allowing it to drain away, treats and stores it and then distributes it for use. This includes water that is collected within the boundaries of a property, from roofs and surrounding surfaces, including areas of hardstanding and pervious paving.

Retention pond – A pond where runoff is detained for a sufficient time to allow settlement and possibly biological treatment of some pollutants.

Runoff – Water flow over the ground surface to the drainage system. This occurs if the ground is impermeable or saturated, or if rainfall is particularly intense.

Section 38 – A legal agreement suppoprted by a bond under Section 38 of the Highways Act 1980 whereby a right of way which has been constructed or which is to be constructed becomes a highway maintainable at the public expense. A publicly maintainable highway may include provisions for drainage of the highway.

Section 104 (S104) – A section within the Water Industry Act (1991) permitting the adoption of a sewer or sewage disposal works by the statutory undertaker.

Section 106 TCPA 1990 – A section within the Town and Country Planning Act 1990 that allows a planning obligation to a local planning authority to be legally binding.

Section 106 WIA 1991 – A key section of the Water Industry Act 1991 that allows the owner/occupier of any premises to have their drains communicate with the public sewers of the sewerage undertaker for that area.

Separate sewer – A sewer for surface water or foul sewage, but not a combination of both.

Sewerage undertaker – This is a collective term relating to the statutory undertaking of water companies that are responsible for sewerage and sewage disposal, including surface water from roofs and yards draining through public sewers.

Sewers for Adoption – A guide agreed between sewerage undertakers and the House Builders Federation specifying the standards to which private sewers need to be constructed to facilitate adoption.

Soakaway – A subsurface structure into which surface water is conveyed to allow infiltration into the ground.

Source control – The control of runoff or pollution at or near its source.

SUDS (sustainable drainage system) – A sequence of management practices and control structures designed to drain surface water in a more sustainable fashion than some conventional techniques.

Surface water management train – The management of runoff in stages as it drains from a site.

Sustainable water management system – The collective term for systems that promote the sustainable management of water. (For the purpose of this book, SUDS and rainwater and greywater use systems are the main sustainable water management systems considered).

Swale – A shallow vegetated channel designed to conduct and retain water, but may also permit infiltration; the vegetation filters particulate matter.

Treatment – Improving the quality of water by physical, chemical and/or biological means.

Watercourse – Any natural or artificial channel that conveys surface water.

Wetland – A pond that has a high proportion of emergent vegetation in relation to open water.

Whole-life costing – Accounting system that considers all the costs (private and social) that accrue to the initiation, provision, operation, maintenance, servicing and decommissioning over the useful life of an asset or a service.

Abbreviations

BSRIA	Building Services Research Information Association
BTSW	Buildings that save water
CDM	Construction (Design and Management) Regulations
COSHH	Control of Substances Hazardous to Health
CSO	combined sewer overflow
DEFRA	Department of Environment, Food and Rural Affairs
DTI	Department of Trade and Industry
EA	Environment Agency
HMSO	Her Majesty's Stationary Office
NBS	National Building Specifications
NAW	National Assembly for Wales
NSWG	National SUDS Working Group
ODPM	Office of the Deputy Prime Minster
Ofwat	Office of Water Services
PPG	Planning Policy Guidance
S106	Section 106 Agreement, Town and Country Planning Act 1990
SEPA	Scottish Environmental Protection Agency
SUDS	Sustainable drainage systems
SUDSWP	Sustainable Drainage Systems Working Party
SWMS	Sustainable water management system
TCPA	Town and Country Planning Act 1990
UDP	Unitary Development Plan
WLC	Whole-life costing

1   Introduction

Sustainable drainage and rainwater/greywater use systems in buildings form a key part of sustainable developments by reducing the impacts that might otherwise occur to surface water runoff and water resources. Sustainable drainage systems (SUDS) are being championed as a solution to existing problems in surface water management. Relative to "traditional" approaches to surface water drainage, SUDS can help reduce the downstream flood and pollution risks that can arise from development, while also helping to replenish groundwater and provide amenity benefits.

CIRIA's recent publications on SUDS and rainwater/greywater use systems have identified the question of eventual ownership of the systems – in particular, who will maintain them – as a major challenge to achieving wider uptake of sustainable water management systems. It is essential to maintain and repair these types of systems properly if they are to perform consistently at design levels, as well as to minimise health and safety hazards.

This publication provides examples of model agreements and simple guidance on their implementation within developments. A model agreement is a legal document that can be used as the basis for agreements between two parties (normally the customer and the maintenance provider) for the maintenance of systems.

The model agreements included here are examples of what can be used. It is not always necessary to use the model agreements, and the wording and the clauses can be amended to reflect specific circumstances.

SCOPE

This guide aims to promote and encourage the sustainable use and management of water within the built environment by providing basic advice on the use and development of maintenance agreements for SUDS alongside simple guidance on their incorporation into developments. The model agreements developed are relevant to the current legislation and policies within England and Wales (at March 2004). A complementary publication, CIRIA C626, has been produced that offers guidance on model agreements for rainwater and greywater use systems.

The specific objectives of providing model agreements and guidance are to:

- encourage the incorporation of sustainable water management systems in new and existing developments
- help developers and/or practitioners incorporate sustainable water management systems into developments
- establish standard approaches to the allocation of responsibilities for the maintenance of sustainable water management systems
- make the adoption and allocation of maintenance for systems more straightforward to allow cost savings and reduce future problems associated with operation and maintenance for clients of the construction industry.

SOURCES OF INFORMATION

This guide and the associated model agreements have been developed from an extensive review of legislation and policy in England and Wales and through consultation with stakeholders from the construction and water industries. The model agreements and guidance documents have been reviewed and agreed by a dedicated project steering group that comprised experienced individuals representing a wide range of stakeholders in the sustainable management of water.

STRUCTURE OF THE BOOK

Chapter 1 – Introduction introduces the guidance and explains the scope of the project. It also provides information on how other guidance can be used to complement this publication and the implementation of the model agreements.

Chapter 2 – Sustainable water management shows how sustainable development can be applied to the water environment and how sustainable water management systems can contribute to sustainable development.

Chapter 3 – What is sustainable drainage? Explains the philosophy behind SUDS and summarises the options that can be used to manage surface water. (More information on components can be obtained from other guidance.)

Chapter 4 – Policy, planning and regulatory considerations considers the current regulatory and planning framework and gives details of the legislation affecting SUDS as well as the planning context.

Chapter 5 – Maintenance of SUDS provides information on the planning and implementation of maintenance regimes.

Chapter 6 – Adoption of SUDS and funding mechanisms indicates some of the ways that stakeholders can adopt SUDS, together with the associated funding mechanisms.

Chapter 7 – SUDS model agreements outlines the development of the model agreements and provides background information to the framework included in the model agreements.

Chapter 8 – Commentary on private SUDS model agreement provides details on how the model agreement may be completed and used.

Model agreements MA1, MA2 and MA3 are provided both as individual booklets and as MS Word documents on CD-ROM, all of which may be found in the pocket at the back of this book. Additionally, an electronic template for the model agreements can be downloaded from <www.ciria.org/suds>.

RELATIONSHIP TO OTHER GUIDANCE

This book forms part of a suite of CIRIA publications relating to both SUDS and rainwater/greywater use systems that provide detailed information on the design and operation of sustainable water management systems.

Related SUDS guidance includes:

- *Sustainable urban drainage systems – design manual for England and Wales*, CIRIA C522 (Martin *et al*, 2000b). Provides guidance on the technical issues surrounding urban drainage systems.

- *Sustainable urban drainage systems – best practice manual*, CIRIA C523 (Martin *et al*, 2001). Provides good practice guidance in the use of SUDS and addresses issues surrounding their use.

- *Source control using constructed pervious surfaces*, CIRIA C582 (Pratt *et al*, 2002). Technical review of existing information on pervious surfaces discussing the hydraulic, structural and water quality issues.

- *Sustainable drainage systems. Hydraulic, structural and water quality advice*, CIRIA C609 (Wilson *et al*, 2004). Technical review of existing information on sustainable drainage systems.

- *Sustainable water management in land use planning*, CIRIA C630 (Samuels *et al*, 2004). Provides guidance on the incorporation of water resource and wastewater treatment issues as part of the planning process for new developments.

Updates on the methods for allocating responsibility for maintenance of SUDS will also be available on CIRIA's SUDS website <www.ciria.org/suds>.

Guidance has also been produced by the National SUDS Working Group. Its "Framework for sustainable drainage systems (SUDS) in England and Wales" (NSWG, 2003) presents a set of core standards and agreements between those public organisations with statutory or regulatory responsibilities relating to SUDS.

It is intended that this publication will evolve into an interim code of practice for SUDS. The ultimate aim is to produce a document similar to *Sewers for adoption* (WRc, 2001).

2   Sustainable water management

INTRODUCTION

The concept of sustainable water management supports economic and social development by optimising the use and management of water for people, agriculture, commerce and industry, while protecting and improving the environment for the future.

The UK Government wants sustainable development to be at the heart of policy making (DETR, 2000a). The national strategy is defined in *A better quality of life – a strategy for sustainable development in the UK* (DETR, 1999). In answering the question "What is sustainable development?", the strategy states:

> At its heart is the simple idea of ensuring a better quality of life for everyone, now and for generations to come.

The strategy specifically identifies water as an example of a renewable resource, which "should be used in ways that do not endanger the resource or cause serious damage or pollution".

Reconciling the water needs of the natural environment with the demands of society poses many difficult challenges. The UK environment is under pressure from many directions: increased housing, increased population density (particularly in the south-east) and extended road networks, all to meet the growing expectations of a population of rising affluence for an improved quality of life. In addition, the realisation and uncertainties of future climate change provide additional drivers for the adoption of a precautionary approach to water management.

DEFINING SUSTAINABLE WATER MANAGEMENT SYSTEMS

Sustainable water management systems are those systems or practices that support the sustainable management of water and contribute positively to the goals of sustainable development. This series of documents is primarily concerned with sustainable drainage systems and rainwater and greywater use systems. In some circumstances, SUDS and rainwater use systems can be combined, although this practice is not widespread within the UK.

DRIVERS FOR SUSTAINABLE WATER MANAGEMENT

Sustainable water management is a concept that includes long-term environmental and social factors in decision-making about the way water is managed or used in the built environment. It considers the quantity and quality of water used and disposed of as well as safeguarding the local environment and amenity. The drivers for sustainable water management are listed in Table 2.1.

Table 2.1 *Drivers for sustainable water management*

Climate change	There is growing evidence that our climate is changing. Household water consumption could well increase as a result of hotter, drier summers. Wetter, colder winters may increase the risk of flooding, and climate change may also alter groundwater and river flow regimes. Sustainable water management systems have the potential to help reduce the impacts of climate change. For example, rainwater and greywater use systems could contribute to the efficient use of resources, while sustainable drainage and the retention of surface water could facilitate groundwater recharge.
Demographic changes	Government projections indicate an increase of around 3.8 million households in England and Wales between 1996 and 2021. The majority of these new households are likely to be smaller, which may increase the overall demand for water and, potentially, the amount of surface water runoff.
Reducing surface runoff and diffuse pollution	Rainwater use systems and sustainable drainage systems could facilitate the attenuation and storage of surface water runoff and potentially reduce the flood risk within a development area. Rainwater reuse systems and sustainable drainage are regarded as preventative systems, controlling both water quantity and water quality at, or close to, the source.
Potential to save costs	Sustainable water management systems designed to reduce and control surface runoff can reduce the need to supplement and increase existing infrastructure to cope with increased flows. They could also reduce the need to upgrade sewage treatment works to treat increased flows as a result of surface water runoff.
Planning requirements	With the introduction of PPG25 *Development and flood risk* (DTLR, 2001a) and the 2002 amendments to Part H of the Building Regulations (DTLR, 2001b), many local authorities are encouraging or requesting the wider use of SUDS to provide the associated environmental benefits.

3   What is sustainable drainage?

Sustainable drainage is an alternative concept in the planning, design and management of surface water drainage systems. The systems work to reduce flood risk and pollution and improve the urban environment for those who live and work in it. The use of source control techniques is integral to SUDS, facilitating an approach to urban drainage that includes a long-term view of the problems and opportunities consistent with sustainable development and building upon natural processes. SUDS are more sustainable than traditional drainage methods because they may:

* reduce the impact of additional urbanisation on the frequency and size of floods

* protect or enhance river and groundwater quality

* be sympathetic to the needs of the local environment and community

* provide a habitat for wildlife

* encourage natural groundwater recharge (where appropriate).

They do this by dealing with runoff in the locality of rainfall or as close to its source as possible. This helps to manage potential flooding and/or pollution at its source.

By minimising the impacts of a development on local surface water drainage systems the use of SUDS may mean that new developments are viable in areas where existing sewerage systems are close to full capacity.

Adopting a holistic approach towards surface water drainage provides the benefits of combined water quality and quantity control, as well as increased amenity value. Ideally, the system should achieve equal standing in all three of these areas, but specific site considerations may mean that these benefits are not always achieved to the same extent.

THE SURFACE WATER MANAGEMENT TRAIN

In comparison with conventional drainage, SUDS offer a greater variety of options to designers. To give some structure to the design process, it is helpful to use the philosophy of the surface water management train. This reinforces and, where possible, follows the natural pattern of drainage. In adopting the surface water management train the following objectives should be met:

* surface water should be returned to the natural environment as soon as possible, promoting natural infiltration and the functioning of the hydrological cycle

* pollutants should be controlled at source before they can be transported and mixed downstream

* the use of impermeable areas should be minimised and, where there is no alternative to their use, they should not be connected to piped drainage systems, but, wherever possible, directed back into the natural water cycle.

If impermeable areas are used, they should be kept clean to prevent pollution of the runoff. If the water is not contaminated, it will not need to be treated before it is returned to the land.

The management train provides a hierarchy of techniques that are listed in order of preference.

1   **Prevention** – the use of good site design and housekeeping measures on individual sites to prevent runoff and pollution (for example, the use of sweeping to remove surface dust from car parks).

2   **Source control** – control of runoff at or very near its source (the use of pervious pavements or green roofs, for example).

3   **Site control** – management of water from several sub-catchments (such as routeing water from roofs and car parks to one large soakaway or infiltration basin for the whole site).

4   **Regional control** – management of runoff from several sites, typically in a detention pond or wetland.

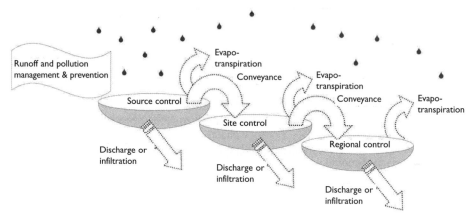

Figure 3.1   *The surface water management train*

The management train shows how runoff can be managed using a series of processes. Each process changes the characteristics of the runoff until it can be discharged. Regional controls should be required only if the runoff cannot be managed locally.

SUDS DRAINAGE COMPONENTS

Ideally, SUDS should not be designed to operate as a number of isolated drainage devices, but should be designed using a holistic approach and operated collectively. Within the philosophy of the surface water management train each component adds to the performance of the whole of the drainage system.

The full range of SUDS that can be used are discussed in detail within CIRIA publications C522 *Sustainable urban drainage systems – design manual for England and Wales* (Martin *et al*, 2000b), C523 *Sustainable urban drainage systems – best practice manual* (Martin *et al*, 2001). Further information can be found on CIRIA's SUDS website <www.ciria.org/suds> and technical detail on the design considerations for SUDS is covered by CIRIA C609 *Sustainable drainage systems. Hydraulic, structural and water quality advice* (Wilson *et al*, 2004).

The most popular methods for managing surface water are summarised in Table 3.1. As each SUDS site has specific requirements, the definitions are not precise.

Table 3.1   *Options for the management of surface water*

Component	Summary	Practical considerations
Prevention/site management	Includes the design and management of a site to reduce the impact of surface runoff, eg minimising impermeable areas, encouraging rainwater use, and good housekeeping to minimise diffuse pollution.	Requires consideration of site design and practices that occur within the site to minimise runoff and diffuse pollution. This will involve good housekeeping practices, eg sweeping hard surfaces.
Filter strips	Strips of ground that treat runoff from adjacent impermeable areas.	The vegetation that forms an essential part of the filter strip needs to be cared for. The grass has to be mown as required and bare patches re-seeded in order to trap pollutants.
Swales	Shallow channels that convey runoff and remove pollutants.	The vegetation that forms an essential part of the swale needs to be cared for. The grass has to be mown as required and bare patches re-seeded in order to trap pollutants in the runoff. Litter should be removed to enhance the swales' amenity value.
Permeable surface	Normally hardstanding structures that allow rainwater to infiltrate through the surface into an underlying storage layer.	Surfaces should be inspected for clogging and water ponding and should be kept clean by sweeping twice a year.
Filter drains	Trenches filled with permeable material into which runoff is collected from the edge of an impermeable area, stored and conveyed.	Surface should be kept clean to prevent the voids from becoming blocked.
Infiltration devices	Devices that temporarily store runoff and allow it to percolate into the ground. They include soakaways, infiltration trenches and infiltration basins as well as swales, filter drains and ponds.	Care should be taken to prevent the ground becoming compacted or the device becoming blocked with silt.
Bioretention areas	Vegetated areas that are designed to collect and treat water before discharge via a piped system or by infiltration to the ground.	The useful life of a bioretention area is related to the frequency of maintenance. Care should be taken of vegetation.
Pipes and accessories	A series of conduits and their accessories normally laid underground and designed to convey surface water to a suitable location for treatment and/or disposal. (These techniques are sustainable where the use of other SUDS techniques is not practicable.)	Care should be taken to ensure that pipes do not become blocked or the flow impeded.
Basins and ponds	Basins are temporary water features. They only fill with water during and after storms. Ponds are permanently wet basins designed to retain stormwater.	Between periods of rainfall, basins can be used for other activities.

SUDS support structures

SUDS components also include various structures that contribute to their function and operation. These should be inspected and maintained to ensure they remain unblocked and undamaged. The main structures and devices are discussed in Table 3.2.

Table 3.2   *SUDS support structures*

Component	Function	Practical considerations
Inlets	Deliver water into the drainage component, which can be open structures or closed, such as pipes.	Deliver water into the drainage component, which can be open structures or closed, such as pipes.
Outlets	Can operate as a control mechanism; they include pipes, weirs and storage structures.	The outlet structure should not be allowed to become blocked.
Silt traps (sediment forebays)	Silt traps can be soft features such as open basins, filter strips and swales. Other structures include small in-line chambers (often called catchpits). Both types of device are designed to protect drainage features.	Where possible, silt should be managed in open traps where monitoring can take place. Maintenance entails regular or site-specific inspections and planned removal of silt.
Flow control devices	The control of flows through a drainage system should be passive and not complicated.	Simple solutions such as orifice plates, slot weirs and sluice controls offer robust solutions to flow control and can easily be managed. Devices should be accessible and easy to maintain without risk and by unskilled personnel.

4   Policy, planning and regulatory considerations

Responsibility for drainage within England and Wales rests with various bodies, including private landowners, local authorities, sewerage undertakers, internal drainage boards and the Environment Agency.

There is no specific legislation covering sustainability considerations for drainage, reflecting the fact that existing drainage law was drawn up before the widespread use of SUDS. This is under review, but the lack of supporting legislation means that there is ambiguity in the allocation of responsibility for the provision, operation and maintenance of SUDS.

RESPONSIBILITIES

In England and Wales, public drainage responsibilities are divided between five main types of organisation:

- local authorities
- highways authorities
- sewerage undertakers
- internal drainage boards
- Environment Agency.

Local authorities act as planning authorities and also have responsibility for local roads (although some highways may come under control of the unitary authority), public landscaping and local land drainage. The Highways Agency controls trunk road drainage, while the sewerage undertakers have a responsibility for the sewers carrying surface water from private impermeable areas such as roofs and drives. Internal drainage boards are responsible for local rivers and land drainage. New development is controlled by local authority planning departments. The Environment Agency has general flood defence and land drainage powers, including the management of flooding issues, but these are primarily in respect of main rivers.

Table 4.1 provides a summary of those organisations with responsibility for drainage.

Table 4.1   *Organisations responsible for drainage in England and Wales*

Name	Function	Authority
Local authority drainage departments	Drainage, flood alleviation and regulation of watercourses, apart from designated main rivers.	Particular responsibilities in drainage districts. Set out in the Land Drainage Act 1991.
Highway authorities	Responsibility to keep the roads (except trunk roads) free from flooding and to make provision for runoff from highways in a proper manner.	Relevant legislation includes the Highways Act 1980 and the Land Drainage Acts 1991 and 1994.
Sewerage undertakers	Responsibility for maintaining a public sewerage system, which includes sewers carrying surface water away from impermeable areas.	Set out in the Water Industry Act 1991 and 1999, which obliges sewerage undertakers to provide and maintain a drainage and sewerage system, and to authorise and charge for the discharge of trade effluent to sewers.
Internal drainage boards	Drainage and flood defence for low-lying land in England and Wales. Regulation of watercourses apart from designated main rivesr.	Set out in the Land Drainage Acts 1991 and 1994, covering maintenance, improvement and operation of drainage systems, conservation and revenue-raising.
Environment Agency	The Agency aims to protect and enhance the environment and to make a positive contribution towards sustainable development in England and Wales. Its water management functions include: • water resources regulation and planning • water quality regulation and planning • flood defence and drainage, maintenance and operations in statutory main rivers.	Powers and duties set out under the Environment Act 1995 and related legislation. Regulation and executive action on water resources, land, water and air quality, flood and coastal defence and flood warning, waste management, navigation, conservation, fisheries and recreation.

LEGISLATION

There is a hierarchy of relevant legislation in England and Wales, which is shown in Table 4.2. Some of the legislation provides opportunities for organisations to adopt sewers and SUDS. The common terms can be found in Table 4.3

Water Industry Act 1991

The Water Industry Act sets out the duties and powers of water companies with respect to water supply and drainage. The Act includes the potential for parts of a SUDS scheme to be defined as a "surface water sewer".

Section 104 of the Water Industry Act allows for a statutory sewerage undertaker to adopt a sewer. In this case, the undertaker needs to determine if the design meets operational and maintenance requirements. Sewerage undertakers facilitate this through stipulating that developers follow the guidance set by *Sewers for adoption*, 5th edition (WRc, 2001). Water companies that adopt the sewer can raise revenue through sewerage charges and payments collected from those connecting to the sewer.

Table 4.2   *Hierarchy of SUDS legislation in England and Wales*

Legislation	Description	Examples
1 **Supranational legislation**	Normally European Directives. They do not themselves form legislation, but are enshrined by member states into their own national legislation	Water Framework Directive (2000/60/EC)
2 **Primary legislation**	Acts of Parliament, which set out the legislation relevant to a particular topic and often provide a framework for implementing secondary legislation.	The Water Industry Act 1991 The Town & Country Planning Act 1990 The Highways Act 1980 Land Drainage Act 1990
3 **Secondary legislation**	Primary regulations that support primary legislation.	The Building Regulations 2000 The Water Supply Regulations 1999
4 **Approved codes of practice**	Interpretation of legislation, which are recognised in law.	CDM Regulations 2000
5 **Planning Policy Guidance**	Set out government thinking and policies. PPGs are material for local authorities in preparing development plans.	PPG3 *Housing (DETR, 2000b)* PPG23 *Planning and pollution control (DoE, 1994)* PPG25 *Development and flood risk (DTLR, 2001a)*

Current legislation allows a sustainable drainage system to be adopted by a sewerage undertaker only if legally it is a sewer. As SUDS combine amenity and environmental benefits with their drainage function, they rarely meet this requirement fully.

Town and Country Planning Act 1990

The Town and Country Planning Act 1990 (as amended by the Planning and Compensation Act 1991) sets out the current framework for planning and development control in England and Wales.

The 1990 Act allows local planning authorities to attach conditions when granting planning permission for developments, which can be used to encourage sustainable drainage. (The Environment Agency can advise and make recommendations to the local authority in this regard.)

Section 106 of the Act allows a legally binding agreement to be entered into between the local planning authority and a third party or parties – commonly referred to as a "planning obligation". The Section 106 planning obligation can:

- restrict the level and type of development
- require specific activities to be carried out in, on, under or over the land
- require money for specified purposes to be paid to the local planning authority (on a specified date or dates or periodically)

These criteria allow the local planning authority to specify, within the obligation, the work to be carried out in connection with sustainable drainage. This is underpinned by the Local Government Act 2000, which imposes on local authorities a duty to promote the improvement of the environment and to contribute to sustainable development of their areas.

Section 106 agreements can be used:

- to specify works in connection with sustainable drainage
- to allow local authorities to work with third parties to carry out their functions. This could include the maintenance of SUDS by sewerage undertakers, landscape maintenance companies and facility managers
- to facilitate financial arrangements and raise monies for this work, which might include:
  - payment of annual contributions or a commuted sum to the local authority for SUDS maintenance
  - the provision of a bond (or insurance to cover a third-party maintenance organisation stopping trading)

The Section 106 agreement for SUDS requires a specification and agreement for the maintenance of the SUDS components and the inclusion of the relevant parties. A model agreement based on the Section 106 Agreement is included within this guidance and the agreement is discussed more fully in Chapter 7.

The Highways Act 1980

The Highways Act sets out legislation with respect to highways. The incorporation of SUDS which involves road drainage usually requires the developer either to enter into an agreement under Section 38 of the Highways Act if involving new development or an agreement under Section 278 of the Act if existing arrangements are to be modified.

Highway authorities have the power to construct, adopt and maintain highway drainage infrastructure. For consistency, each highway authority sets standards which developers must follow to ensure that highways and drainage systems are satisfactorily constructed, safe and easily maintainable.

Summary of common terms

Section 38   Highways Act 1980 – adoption of highway drainage.

Section 104   Water Industry Act 1991 – adoption of works by statutory undertaker.

Section 106   Water Industry Act, 1991 – right to connect to public sewers.

Section 106   Town and Country Planning Act 1990 – planning obligation for restricting development.

PLANNING AND BUILDING CONTROL

Development of land requires planning permission from the local planning authority (under the Town and Country Planning Act 1990). The development of land for any significant building or engineering project is likely to give rise to drainage issues, and the adequacy of drainage from a site will be a "material consideration" in the determination of a planning application.

The application of the Town and Country Planning Act is delivered through Planning Policy Guidance (PPG) Notes that set out the Government's policies on different aspects of planning. Local planning authorities must take their content into account in preparing their development plans. The guidance may also be material to decisions on individual planning applications and appeals.

Consideration of SUDS needs to be included in development plans. The development control process can be used as a lever to promote the wider implementation of SUDS. Policies can be included in planning documents (structure plans and local plans) and more detailed guidance can be provided in supplementary planning guidance or detailed development briefs for a particular site.

The planning framework for SUDS is set out in PPG25 *Development and flood risk* (DTLR, 2001a), which encourages the incorporation of SUDS into developments.

PPG25 Development and flood risk

PPG25 sets out government policy on the role of land-use planning to reduce risks from flooding and provides specific guidance on the need to manage surface water drainage from developments. The overall aim is to avoid development in areas at risk from flooding and to manage any risks in an acceptable way.

The Guidance Note identifies the contribution SUDS can make to preventing increases in runoff from new developments and to general sustainability. It encourages teamwork between local authorities, the Environment Agency, sewerage undertakers, navigation authorities and prospective developers to facilitate sustainable drainage.

PPG25 explains that appropriately designed SUDS can improve the amenity and wildlife value of development and improve the attractiveness of developments. In some cases the use of SUDS can allow a development to proceed that would otherwise be refused because of the increased flood risk caused by runoff.

The requirement to take SUDS into account both at the inception and at detailed planning stages of development is highlighted, as is the need for:

- integration of SUDS into the overall site concept and layout
- investigation and subsequent remediation of contaminated land
- agreements on adoption, maintenance and operation of the systems
- monitoring long-term performance.

A new development planning system is proposed for England and Wales in 2004. PPGs will be replaced by Planning Policy Statements (PPS). These will be focused statements of policy, supported by technical guidance.

Building Regulations

The Building Regulations 2000 were amended in 2002 to include Requirement H3, Rainwater Drainage, which refers to the preferred types of outfall in priority order, and Approved Document H includes some guidance to encourage the incorporation of SUDS in the decision-making process for designing drainage systems.

The preferred option is to drain the rainwater to an adequate soakaway or another infiltration system. If a site cannot drain to an infiltration system, then the next favoured option is to dispose of the water to a watercourse. Where this is not feasible, the last option is to drain the rainwater to a sewer.

THE NATIONAL SUDS WORKING GROUP

The National SUDS Working Group (NSWG) was established in 2001 to address the perceived issues impeding the widespread use of SUDS in England and Wales. It includes representatives from:

- Office of the Deputy Prime Minister
- Department for Environment, Food and Rural Affairs
- Department for Transport
- National Assembly for Wales
- Office of Water Services
- Water UK
- Local Government Association
- Planning Officers Society
- English Nature
- Association of Highway Authorities
- House Builders Federation
- CIRIA
- Environment Agency.

The group aims to formulate proposals for a core set of standards and agreements between those public organisations with statutory or regulatory responsibilities relating to the disposal of surface water. The group produced a Framework Document for SUDS in England in Wales in May 2003. CIRIA and the NSWG have been working together to develop some of the elements of the Interim Code of Practice for SUDS, and this project's model agreements were included with the document for consultation.

The Framework Document provides guidance on planning, regulation and consents, legal issues, and ownership and maintenance. It should be seen as complementary to the CIRIA SUDS manuals.

5 Maintenance

A key factor in ensuring the successful implementation of SUDS is the ongoing operation and maintenance of the various system components. Maintenance of SUDS is generally no more difficult than maintaining piped systems, although they have different requirements and may demand different skill sets. Effective maintenance helps ensure that SUDS continue to function as they were intended and keeps the hydraulic capacity and pollutant removal efficiency of the systems at design levels.

Before a maintenance regime for SUDS can be implemented a handover inspection should be arranged to ensure that the client has a robust SUDS scheme that is unlikely to fail due to errors in design and/or implementation.

Most SUDS components should be inspected periodically to ensure litter, siltation and other blockages are not adversely affecting the operation of the system. This does not have to be onerous, but it does enable corrective action to be taken in a timely manner.

This chapter provides an overview on maintenance requirements for SUDS. For more detailed information on maintenance, refer to CIRIA publications C522, C523 or C609.

INSPECTIONS

Routine inspections should be carried out regularly depending on the type of SUDS component and the site conditions. Some components, such as infiltration devices, do not need to be checked so often.

The Construction (Design and Management) Regulations 2000 require designers to consider risks during the construction and maintenance of structures. SUDS schemes must comply with these requirements.

A review of health and safety considerations for construction and maintenance should be undertaken and designers must make contractors and others aware of risks in a health and safety file. The health and safety file is a record of the key health and safety risks that need to be managed during maintenance work.

MAINTENANCE

The design of SUDS should facilitate the safe and convenient access by personnel and construction plant. Landscaped or "green" SUDS features are generally visible, so problems are usually obvious; most can be remedied using standard landscaping methods.

SUDS maintenance can be undertaken as part of normal site care by site staff or landscape contractors. Landscape maintenance specification such as those included in the National Building Specifications (NBS), can be adapted to suit SUDS. More engineered features such as filter drains will require traditional maintenance. Further details on maintenance for SUDS components can be found in Table 5.1.

Routine maintenance

A three-year landscape maintenance contract is becoming increasingly common. It promotes continuity of care and is the preferred approach for both landscaped and engineered features. Most site tasks are based on monthly site visits except when vegetation growth requires visits at shorter intervals. Certain SUDS maintenance tasks, eg silt management, require less frequent attention, but they still need to be included in the contract period to ensure continuity and financial planning.

Major overhauls

Engineered SUDS components (particularly infiltration and treatment systems) may require a major overhaul of the system at some stage during their design life. Tasks may include the removal and replacement of clogged filters and geotextiles. The timing of this is typically between three and 25 years, depending on the technique and factors, such as the type of catchment and sediment load.

Maintenance plan

A maintenance plan provides a way of budgeting and specifying maintenance against certain objectives for a SUDS scheme. The document should explain the function of the SUDS scheme and discuss health and safety and management implications, in addition to any specific ecological issues.

The specification and schedule of work

The specification details how work is to be carried out and contains clauses that give general instruction to the contractor, these should not be long or too onerous but must be sufficient to ensure the ongoing operation of the SUDS scheme. Clauses may include specific tasks to be completed after construction but should also include the tasks and actions required to maintain the site. The schedule of work details particular activities and the frequency required to achieve an acceptable standard should be set out in the schedule of work.

Waste management

Many SUDS schemes promote sedimentation or siltation and these processes should be managed. Organic waste should preferably be used around the SUDS scheme to form wildlife piles. If this is not practical, the waste should be compacted or, as a last resort, disposed of to a licensed landfill site.

Inorganic silt (from closed silt traps, basins, ponds and wetlands) is generally the most polluted material. It should be stacked on site, dewatered and then spread on banks and berms to change levels; if this is not practicable, it should be removed from site.

Sediment waste arisings from systems should be treated as a controlled waste and so are subject to control under the Waste Management Licensing Regime. In certain circumstances, the Special Waste Regulations 1996 may also be relevant.

Further information on waste management can be found in CIRIA C609 (Wilson *et al*, 2004) and the NSWG Framework Document (NSWG, 2003).

All maintenance of SUDS and waste arisings must be undertaken within the relevent statutory frameworks – advice can be sought from the Environment Agency.

Table 5.1 *Maintenance requirements for SUDS components*

	Filter strips and swales	Freq
Considerations	Filter strips and swales accumulate silt naturally due to their primary position in the SUDS management train.	
Regular maintenance	• Grass cutting (typically 100–150 mm) • litter removal • removal of excess silt • inlet and outlet cleaning (if necessary) • disposal and management of silt.	R/M M M R/S R
Inspections	Regular inspections of the filter strip or swale should be undertaken. Inspections should: • identify erosion and deposition • identify areas of excess waterlogging.	 R R/M
Remedial/ occasional maintenance	Remedial work may include: • reinstatement to edgings • reinstatement of levels and turf due to erosions • realignment of erosion controls.	
Overhaul		
	Permeable surfaces	
Considerations	The use of grit and salt may adversely affect the treatment and drainage potential of pavement. Use of weedkillers may disrupt the biological breakdown of contaminants in the sub-base.	
Regular maintenance	• Surface should be cleaned to keep voids clean using brush and vacuum (start of spring and winter) • good housekeeping and litter removal • control of weeds and cut surrounding grass (35–50 mm) • remove accumulated silt from site and dispose of appropriately.	B M/S R R
Inspections	• Any inlet/outlet should be inspected to check for blockages • surface infiltration should be monitored following heavy rain.	R/M R/M
Remedial/ occasional maintenance	If infiltration is found to be decreasing significantly, then: • remove permeable paving and clean • remove bedding grit and geotextile and dispose of safely • replace geotextile, replace grit bedding layer.	
Overhaul	Likely to be every 15–25 years (or greater).	
	SUDS support structures	
Regular maintenance	• Litter removal • strimming of grass adjacent to structure (1 m radius) • removal of impending debris/silts • ensure free moving parts.	M M M M
Inspections	• Inspection for evidence of erosion/damage or blockage.	M
Remedial/ occasional maintenance	• Repair damage/erosion to structure of surrounding banks.	

Table 5.1 *Maintenance requirements for SUDS components* (continued)

	Infiltration devices	**Freq**
Considerations	This includes filter drains, infiltration trenches and soakaways. Grounds around these devices should be kept clear of silt to prevent it getting washed into the device, which will eventually reduce the permeability of the soil.	
Regular maintenance	• Litter removal • surface kept clear of silt and voids kept clear • control of weeds and cutting of surrounding grass (35–75 mm).	M B R
Inspections	Regular inspection should be undertaken, particularly after significant storm events. Inspections should identify: • areas that are not working properly, blockages • erosion around outfalls • areas where damage is evident • silt/vegetation accumulation.	 M/S M/S M/S M
Remedial/ occasional maintenance	If the permeability of the system appears to be reducing with time, then remedial action may have to be considered, including: • removal of stone above geotextile in infiltration trenches • removal and safe disposal of geotextile • replacement of clean stone top layer.	
Overhaul		

	Basins and ponds	**Freq**
Considerations	The maintenance of ponds and wetlands depends on the type of effect desired. Wetland management is based on a "little and often" approach.	
Regular maintenance	• Litter removal • regular grass cutting (basins 35–75 mm) • management of meadows for wildlife • inlet and outlet cleaning • clearance of bankside vegetation • control and removal of aquatic plants (if required).	M/S R A/B M/S R R
Inspections	Maintenance depends on the nature of the landscaping employed. If planted with low ground cover and shrubs, twice-yearly inspection and repair should be sufficient. • Inlet and outlet structures should be inspected twice a year and after large storms • silt accumulation should be monitored.	 B/R/S M
Remedial/ occasional maintenance	• Silt accumulation should be removed when required • damage or erosion should be repaired • care should be taken to avoid damaging any liner • repair or rehabilitation of inlets, outlets and overflows.	
Overhaul	The frequency to overhaul or even undertake the remedial activities is difficult to determine. This may be a regular activity or undertaken every three years.	

Key to abbreviations in Frequency column

A: annually; B: biannually; M: monthly; R: as required; S: following significant storm event

6 Adoption of SUDS and funding mechanisms

The question of who manages and maintains sustainable drainage systems has long been thought of as a major barrier to greater uptake of SUDS in England and Wales. This project and the NSWG's Interim Code of Practice for SUDS are designed to establish a framework to simplify the allocation of responsibilities for their long-term maintenance.

The long-term safe maintenance of SUDS differs from that of traditionally piped systems and there are opportunities for a wider range of organisations to become involved in it.

The various possibilities for the adoption of SUDS are discussed below.

LOCAL AUTHORITIES

Including open space within development sites is common practice within the UK and can make it easier to add SUDS features. These can enhance the nature conservation and amenity value of the development and contribute positively to biodiversity action plans.

A local authority that is adopting an open space could also adopt SUDS features. The use of the open space for other purposes should not adversely affect the proper operation and maintenance of the SUDS. There is in any case a requirement to consider and plan for the long-term maintenance of SUDS.

As discussed in Chapter 4, Section 106 of the Town and Country Planning Act 1990 provides a suitable mechanism for securing funding (from developers) so that an appropriately designed SUDS scheme can be maintained and managed by the local authority. This approach requires a maintenance plan, a hazard risk assessment and the establishment of financial mechanisms to provide an income stream to cover the management and maintenance of the SUDS feature for a set time.

Local authorities can fund ongoing maintenance through agreements, which may include a commuted sum (taken from the developer) or a robust bonded arrangement. These facilitate the adoption of areas within an acceptable timeframe without placing too great a burden on the local authority. A model agreement for adopting SUDS under Section 106 is included at the back of the book and on the CD-ROM.

Financial mechanisms

Several research projects are being undertaken to determine the maintenance and operation costs of SUDS components over their design life.

Whole-life costing (WLC) involves identifying future costs and referring them back to present-day values using standard accounting techniques. It is used for valuing the total costs of assets that have regular operating and/or cyclical maintenance costs, based on formalised maintenance programmes.

WLC may be used to estimate total lifetime expenditure and can reduce the uncertainties associated with developing adoption agreements and commuted sum contributions.

HIGHWAY AUTHORITIES

Highway authorities do have powers to adopt SUDS, but the funding mechanisms for the maintenance need to be resolved. It may be possible to effect this through a commuted sum.

Within Section 38, highway authorities or local authorities can seek confirmation that the SUDS components are designed and constructed in accordance with agreed specifications.

SEWERAGE UNDERTAKERS

In order for the sewerage undertaker to adopt a conventional piped system and to undertake its maintenance, the developer needs to construct the sewer in accordance with the agreed specifications set out in *Sewers for adoption* (WRc, 2001).

The standards and specification in *Sewers for adoption* do not address SUDS, as sewerage undertakers are generally constrained to adopt only piped systems. There is uncertainty as to whether SUDS – and infiltration systems in particular – have a proper outfall and fall within the legal definition of a "sewer" (as defined in the Water Industry Act 1991), which would allow them to be adopted by the sewerage undertaker.

PRIVATE ORGANISATIONS

In the case of a private landowner or management company, the funding can be generated from a specific maintenance contract (in a similar way to landscaped features) or budgeted allocation. This arrangement would need to be bonded through a Section 106 agreement of the Town and Country Planning Act to enable the local authority to take over maintenance should the arrangement fail. Sums could be drawn from this bond to fund maintenance as necessary.

7   SUDS model agreements

DEVELOPMENT OF MODEL AGREEMENTS

The model agreements developed for this publication have been based on a detailed legislation review and consultation exercise. The legislation review highlighted the most effective legal framework for the agreements. Consultation with interested parties provided a list of potential scenarios where agreements would need to be used. The model agreements are based on current legislation (March 2004).

No conditions have been placed on the maintainer for the performance of the SUDS, as this would be difficult to measure. Instead, it is assumed that if the SUDS are properly designed, constructed and maintained they will perform in a satisfactory manner.

AIMS

The aim of these model agreements is to improve uptake by providing a mechanism for maintenance. Model agreements have been developed for the following situations:

- implementation and maintenance of SUDS through the planning process, either as a planning obligation under Section 106 of the Town and Country Planning Act 1990 or as a condition attached to planning permission

- implementation and maintenance of SUDS between two or more parties (outside of the requirements for planning permission), ie private SUDS model agreement.

The Section 106 model agreement and the maintenance framework agreement are provided for where SUDS and their maintenance are required as a result of the planning process. The private model agreement is intended for use outside this planning framework. A summary of the documents (and their references) required for these two situations is provided in Figure 7.1.

Guidance and commentary on applying the private SUDS model agreement is provided in Chapter 8. Guidance on applying the planning-based model agreements is provided within the documents themselves.

MODEL AGREEMENTS PRODUCED

SUDS model agreements have been developed through this project for the situations indicated in Table 7.1.

Table 7.1   *Model agreements produced*

Reference	Title and description
SUDS MA1	Planning obligation – incorporating SUDS provisions Implementation and maintenance of SUDS either as a planning obligation under Section 106 of the Town and Country Planning Act 1990 or as a condition attached to planning permission.
SUDS MA2	SUDS maintenance framework agreement Legal framework that defines which body takes over and maintains the SUDS.
SUDS MA3	Private SUDS model agreement Implementation and maintenance of SUDS between two or more parties (outside of the requirements for planning permission), ie private SUDS model agreement.

If the council requires SUDS as part of the planning process, two methods are available.

1   As a planning obligation under Section 106 of the Town and Country Planning Act 1990.

2   By a condition attached to the planning permission.

The most appropriate method will depend on the scale of the development. The documents provided to help the process are summarised below.

1   Planning obligation

Planning obligation under Section 106 of the Town and Country Planning Act 1990 (SUDS MA1)	This is a legal agreement to enforce a properly implemented and maintained SUDS scheme
Maintenance framework agreement (SUDS MA2)	This document sets out the responsibilities of the parties for implementation and maintenance

2   Condition to planning permission

Condition added to planning permission which requires SUDS	This requires the developer to use SUDS within the development
Maintenance agreement	An agreement should be produced to facilitate ongoing maintenance

The owner of a drainage scheme has a responsibility for ongoing maintenance. If the planning process does not define implementation and maintenance of the SUDS, the document below can be used to set out the maintenance requirements of a SUDS scheme.

Private model agreement (SUDS MA3)	This document is a private agreement between two (or more) parties to facilitate ongoing maintenance

Figure 7.1   *Summary of documents (shaded boxes are documents provided with this guidance)*

CHOICE OF ROUTE FOR SUDS DEVELOPMENT AND MAINTENANCE

The choice of model agreement and the mechanism for implementation will usually be determined by the local planning authority. A schematic showing the various processes involved is shown as Figure 7.2 where SUDS are required as part of the planning process. Figure 7.3 shows the methods available to implement SUDS maintenance where they are not required as part of the planning process.

Where there is a requirement to implement SUDS, the local planning authority has two routes available to ensure that the SUDS are properly implemented and maintained. These are:

● through an agreement under Section 106 of the Town and Country Planning Act

● by a condition to planning permission.

Where the scheme is small or the SUDS scheme is simple, the use of a planning condition may be the best option. However, planning conditions can be appealed against and enforcement can be difficult. When SUDS are required outside of the Section 106 process, the private SUDS model agreement may be used to facilitate maintenance.

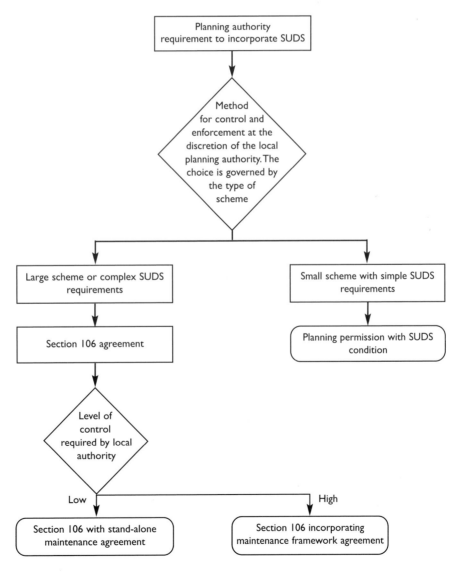

Figure 7.2   *Model agreement options with SUDS as a requirement of planning permission*

Where the development is larger or the SUDS scheme is complex the Section 106 approach should be used. With a large development scheme, it is likely that a Section 106 agreement would already be implemented for other issues such as improved public transport or education. The Section 106 route requires negotiations and legal preparatory work in advance of the development taking place, but offers more security as it may only be varied by agreement. It also allows for financial contributions in the form of a bond or a periodic payment.

Within the Section 106 model agreement there are alternative methods as to whether the maintenance agreement is included as part of the Section 106 agreement or is stand-alone. Again, this is at the discretion of the local planning authority. This choice should be governed by the degree of control the local planning authority would like to have over the maintenance issues. Where greater control is required, the maintenance framework agreement should be used and incorporated as part of the Section 106 agreement.

Where local planning authorities seek to incorporate SUDS within developments using these methods they should seek independent legal advice to ensure that the most appropriate method is used. Some changes to the standard document will almost certainly be required for each individual situation.

The private SUDS model agreement may be used by a developer or site owner to ensure proper maintenance of the site drainage scheme. It may be used for either existing or new developments.

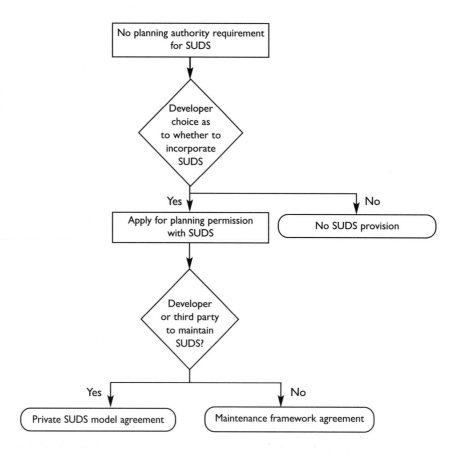

Figure 7.3 *Model agreement options when SUDS are not required as part of planning permission*

SUDS AS A CONDITION TO PLANNING PERMISSION

A separate model agreement is not necessary when the SUDS are required as a condition to planning permission. A form of maintenance agreement will be required, which could be the maintenance framework agreement (SUDS MA2), although different forms of agreements can be used. This will allow the developer to enter into agreements to provide for maintenance of the SUDS to the satisfaction of the local authority.

A schematic showing this route is included as Figure 7.4.

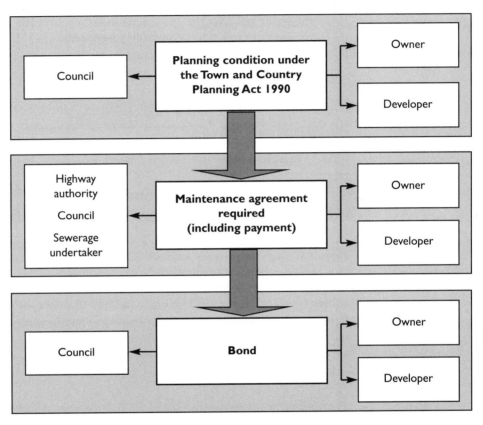

Figure 7.4   *SUDS as a planning condition with a stand-alone maintenance agreement and bond*

TCPA SECTION 106 MODEL AGREEMENT

As explained in Figure 7.2, there are two alternative methods of providing for SUDS within the Section 106 model agreement. These are:

- Section 106 agreement with a stand-alone maintenance framework agreement and bond
- Section 106 agreement incorporating the maintenance framework agreement.

The first method envisages an obligation within the Section 106 agreement to enter into the maintenance agreement that would then be a stand-alone document supported by a bond (to act as a financial guarantee). If the maintenance agreement is stand-alone, then the provisions of the 1990 Act with regard to periodic payments cannot apply, so the bond must be used. Figure 7.5 illustrates this method.

Note that there is a statutory requirement for anyone with "an interest" in the land to be a party to the Section 106 deed.

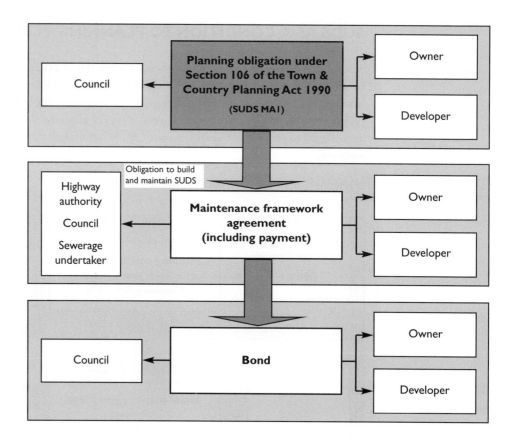

Figure 7.5 *Section 106 agreement with a stand-alone maintenance agreement and bond*

The second method proposes the incorporation of the model agreement into the Section 106 agreement itself. This ties in the local planning authority, which would have the powers of enforcement and the ability to levy the periodic charges as part of the Section 106 provisions. There are three options proposed within this arrangement for maintaining the SUDS. A bond could also be considered as a financial safety net if required. Figure 7.6 shows this method of implementation.

The options for maintenance of the SUDS defined within this method are as follows:

● Option 1 – SUDS maintained by the council

● Option 2 – SUDS vested in the council

● Option 3 – SUDS maintained by a third party.

Within Option 1 the council approves the design of the SUDS and then is responsible for maintenance following payment of a sum. Option 2 vests the SUDS in the council, which is then responsible for the system. Option 3 allows for other organisations to maintain the SUDS to a standard approved by the council. A bond is put in place to provide security in case of failure.

The Section 106 agreement itself is formed of the agreement document and a number of schedules. Different schedules are required, depending on which of the maintenance options is chosen. Table 7.1 shows those parts of the document that are required for each option.

Table 7.2   *Documents required for each option*

Option	Agreement	Schedule 1	Schedule 2	Schedule 3
1 – SUDS maintained by council	Required for each option.	Map showing the land and SUDS system. Required for each option.	Required. Covenants from owner/developer to the council.	Required. Covenants from council to owner/developer.
2 – SUDS vested in council			Required. Vesting of SUDS in the council.	Not required.
3 – SUDS maintained by a third party			Required. Covenant from owner/developer to the council.	Required. Details of maintenance scheme to be included.

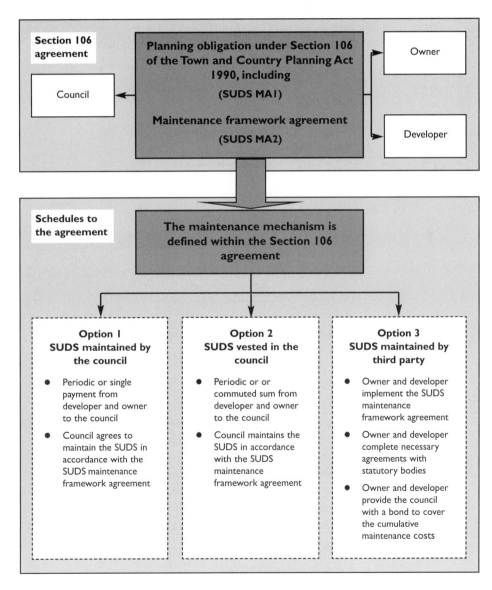

Figure 7.6   *Section 106 agreement incorporating the maintenance framework agreement*

MAINTENANCE FRAMEWORK AGREEMENT

The maintenance framework agreement is the legal framework that defines which body takes over and maintains the SUDS. This can be the highway authority, the council or the sewerage undertaker. The agreement is summarised as Figure 7.7.

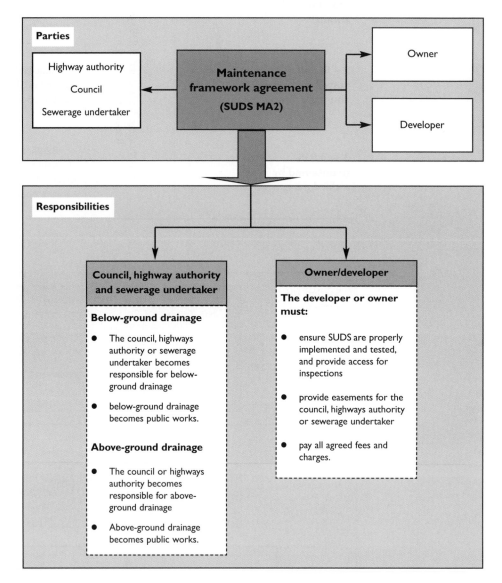

Figure 7.7 *The maintenance framework agreement*

PRIVATE SUDS MODEL AGREEMENT

The private SUDS model agreement is a simple contract between the property owner/ tenant (customer) and the maintenance provider (the maintainer). It is set up chiefly to facilitate continuing maintenance of SUDS that are in private (freehold) ownership. The owner could be a large landowner, a housing association, corporate body or single household. This contract sets out the responsibilities of the parties, the number of maintenance visits and the charges for the services. A diagram showing the main elements of the agreement appears as Figure 7.8. The contract has two main components:

- the model agreement
- the schedule.

The model agreement places obligations on both the maintainer and the customer. The maintainer's obligations are to ensure that all maintenance duties are carried out effectively as instructed in the schedule of work. The customer's obligations include the provision of access to the SUDS and to ensure that all ancillary drainage (such as drainpipes) are also adequately maintained.

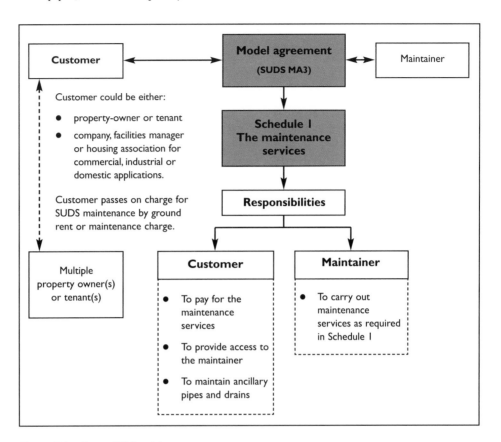

Figure 7.8   *Private SUDS model agreement*

Responsibility for maintenance

Owners of all drainage systems are responsible for their maintenance and proper upkeep. If maintenance is not performed properly owners may be liable for damage caused due to failure of their drainage system.

Details of the services to be provided are set out in the schedule, which can be amended to provide specific information about the maintenance tasks required. It should specify the activities that should be undertaken during each maintenance visit, such as grass cutting, clearance of debris and removal of silt. The customer may also require other activities to be carried out such as inspection of manholes or of other parts of the drainage system and may request a maintenance report to be provided. Commentary and guidance on the private SUDS model agreement is provided in Chapter 8.

On the transfer of ownership of the property, it is important that the new owner continues to maintain the SUDS properly. There is no facility for the agreement to be transferred between owners, although it can be terminated by giving 30 days' notice. Details of the agreement can then be passed to the new owner of the property.

In some circumstances a facilities manager will be responsible for maintaining the SUDS within an estate of properties. In this case, the facilities manager will be the customer for the purposes of the model agreement. Funds to pay for maintenance of the SUDS may be raised via the ground rent or other similar charge.

8   Commentary on the private SUDS model agreement (MA3)

COMMENTARY ON THE MODEL AGREEMENT

Details of parties	
	The details of both parties (maintainer and customer) should be entered into the tables. This defines the two parties to the agreement who are from here on referred to as the "maintainer" and the "customer".
Section 1 – Definitions	
	These clauses set out the definitions of the key terms used in the agreement as well as the annual maintenance charge and the commencement date.
	The specific actions required to maintain the SUDS are set out in Schedule 1.
	The agreed *annual maintenance charge should be entered* in the space provided in Clause 1.2.
	The commencement date is the date from which the agreement comes into force. *This should be filled in using the space provided* in Clause 1.3. This may or may not be the date of the agreement.
Section 2 – Maintenance services	
Clauses 2.1, 2.2 and 2.3	Section 2 sets out the terms and conditions under which the maintainer services will be carried out.
	The working hours during which it is acceptable for the maintenance to be carried out *should be entered in the space provided in* Clause 2.2. This ensures that the work will not be carried out at unsociable times unless in the case of an emergency and that the customer will be able to provide access.
	Clause 2.3 requires the maintainer to respond to any request for additional services promptly. This is to allow the customer to call on the maintainer to help resolve an unexpected maintenance problem. *The maximum response time should be entered in the space provided.* This should be fixed taking into account the maintainer's mobilisation time and the likely urgency of repair.
Clauses 2.4, 2.5 and 2.6	Clauses 2.4 and 2.4 set out that the agreement:
	• takes precedence over the maintainer's standard conditions of sale
	• does not apply to any modifications to the SUDS.
	Clause 2.6 states that the maintainer must give 24 hours' notice before carrying out work on site. This is to give the customer time to arrange access.

Clause 2.7	This clause specifies the time interval between the commencement date and the first maintenance visit. *This time interval should be entered.*
Section 3 – Maintenance charges	
Clause 3.1	These clauses set out the terms that apply to the payment of the maintenance charges. The agreed charges will be paid every year in advance, on or before the commencement date and the same date of every following year that the agreement is kept in force.
Clause 3.2	This clause sets out that services in addition to those set out in Schedule 1 will be subject to extra charges under the maintainer's usual terms.
Clause 3.3	This clause sets out the maintainer's right to amend the charges for the following year by written notice, which is to be given at least 30 days before the annual renewal of the agreement. The customer is under no obligation to renew the agreement for a further year. The maintainer may terminate the agreement if the customer does not pay the maintenace charges on time. The customer is given 30 days from the due date to pay the maintenance charge.
Section 4 – Maintainer's obligations	
	These clauses set out the maintainer's obligations under the agreement, which, in summary, are to: • carry out the maintenance in a proper, diligent and workmanlike manner • use appropriate equipment and competent staff • indemnify the customer against any losses due to the maintainer's neglect or default • rectify any breach of the agreement identified by the customer.
Section 5 – Customer's obligations	
	These clauses set out the customer's obligations under the agreement, which, in summary, are to: • pay the charges promptly • provide access • not modify the equipment significantly • maintain associated drainage and pipework.

Section 6 – Commencement and term of the agreement	
	This clause sets out that the agreement will run for a year at a time or until one party gives 30 days' prior written notice.
	If the customer moves property it is advised that he terminates the contract (giving 30 days' notice) and notifies the incoming owner/ tenant of the agreement in advance to enable him to enter into a similar agreement.

Section 7 – VAT	
	These clauses set out that VAT should be paid in addition to any charges unless otherwise stated.

Section 8 – Termination	
	These clauses set out the reasons for which the agreement may be terminated immediately and can be summarised as follows: <ul><li>the customer or maintainer fails to comply in any respect with the agreement</li><li>either party dies or becomes bankrupt</li><li>either party is subject to liquidation or receivership.</li></ul>

Section 9 – Termination consequences	
	This section sets out the consequences of termination of the agreement. **Note** It is essential that even if the agreement is terminated, the drainage system is still properly maintained. Owners of drainage systems may be liable for damage if they do not maintain an effective drainage system.
Clauses 9.1 and 9.2	These clauses set out that within 30 days of termination the maintainer must produce a final account taking into account: <ul><li>any refund due to the customer for maintenance paid for in advance but not yet carried out. This should be calculated in proportion to the total number of activities paid for</li><li>all arrears due to the maintainer under this agreement.</li></ul> This account should be settled within 30 days of receipt of the final account.
Clauses 9.3 and 9.4	These clauses give both parties the entitlement to use the rights granted by the agreement, including enforcing the other party's liabilities and other common law rights available for redress as a consequence of breach of this agreement.

Section 10 – Discretion	
	This clause sets out that any discretion or opinion exercised will only be binding if it is agreed in writing by both parties.

Section 11 – Change of address	
	Under this clause both parties must give notice of a change of address or contact detail at the earliest possible opportunity, within a maximum of 48 hours.

Section 12 – Notices	
	These clauses set out the conditions that must be met for a notice to be considered to have been served.

Section 13 – Proper law and jurisdiction	
	English law and the jurisdiction of English courts apply to this agreement.

Section 14 – Interest	
	This clause sets out the rate of interest payable on late payments. The interest rate is set by specifying an additional percentage point above the base lending rate of a named bank. *The additional interest rate, name of the bank, minimum total interest rate per year and type of base lending rate (daily/monthly/yearly etc) to be used should be inserted in the spaces provided.*

Section 15 – Force majeure	
	This clause sets out that either party whose actions are prevented by *force majeure* must give prompt notice and use their best endeavours to carry out the action, but will be excused if these fail.

Section 16 – Whole agreement	
	This section declares that the agreement does not rely on any other spoken or written agreements between the parties.

Section 17 – Arbitration	
	This clause allows the parties to refer disputes to a commonly agreed independent arbitrator, or, where one cannot be agreed upon, to an arbitrator nominated by the president of the Chartered Institution of Arbitrators.

CIRIA C625

Section 18 – Subcontracting	
Clause 18.1	This clause sets out that the maintainer may subcontract its obligations subject to the customer's prior written consent.
Clause 18.2	This clause sets out that the customer may only assign or delegate any of the agreement to another party with the prior written consent of the maintainer.

Section 19 – Third party rights	
	No other parties may acquire any rights from this agreement.

Section 20 – Variation	
	This clause allows the parties to refer disputes to a commonly agreed arbitrator, or, where one cannot be agreed upon, to an arbitrator nominated by the president of the Chartered Institution of Arbitrators.

Signatures	
	A representative of the customer and of the maintainer should sign and insert their name and date of signature in the spaces provided.

COMMENTARY ON SCHEDULE 1

Section 1 – Details of the SUDS	
Clause 1	Details of the SUDS should be included in this section. Any drawings, maintenance manuals or other guidance should be included as Appendix 1 and a brief description of this information provided.

Section 2 – Health, safety and environment	
Clauses 2.1 and 2.2	Maintenance of this equipment may be hazardous if not correctly managed. Risk assessments should be carried out by the maintainer in advance of carrying out this maintenance work, and all procedures should be strictly followed. A list of any site-specific precautions should be included in the schedule. This should include any information that is particularly relevant to the site, such as the storage of hazardous substances. There are unlikely to be any site-specific precautions in the domestic environment. More information about risk assessments and health and safety in the workplace is available from the Health and Safety Executive (see <www.hse.gov.uk> for details).
Clauses 2.3 and 2.4	These clauses relate to the environmental impact associated with the disposal of any materials removed from the system. These items should be disposed of in a safe and proper manner. The maintainer shall ensure that all relevant licences and consents from environment regulatory bodies have been received prior to commencement of any maintenance work. More information about waste disposal is available from the Environment Agency (see <www.environment-agency.gov.uk> for details).

Section 3 – The maintenance services	
	This section sets out the activities to be carried out as part of the maintenance service. For further details see Section 5. Here the detail of the activities required and the frequency with which they should be carried out should be entered. This may include activities such as: • removing silt from silt traps • cutting grass • removing litter and other detritus • inspecting chambers.

9　References and further information

BETTESS, R (1996) *Infiltration drainage – manual of good practice*. R156, CIRIA, London

DEPARTMENT OF THE ENVIRONMENT (1994) *Planning and pollution control.* Planning Policy Guidance note 23, HMSO, London

DETR (1999) *A better quality of life – a strategy for sustainable development for the UK.* HMSO, London (ISBN 0-10-143452-9)

DETR (2000a) *Sustainable development – what it is and what you can do.* Department of the Environment, Transport and the Regions, London

DETR (2000b) *Housing.* Planning Policy Guidance note 3, Stationery Office, London

DTLR (2001a) *Development and flood risk.* PPG25, Stationery Office, London

DTLR (2001b) *Building Regulations 2000. Approved Document H: drainage and waste disposal.* Stationery Office, London

GREENBELT GROUP OF COMPANIES (2001) *SUDS – a solution for their management and maintenance.* Greenbelt Group of Companies, Glasgow

GREENBELT GROUP OF COMPANIES (2002) *Management and maintenance agreement in respect of amenity areas.* Greenbelt Group of Companies, Glasgow

HALL, M J, HOCKIN, D L and ELLIS, J B (1993) *Design of flood storage reservoirs.* Book 14, CIRIA, London

HR WALLINGFORD (2003) *The operation and maintenance of sustainable drainage infrastructure and associated costs.* SR 626, HR Wallingford, Wallingford

MARTIN, P, TURNER, B, WADDINGTON, K, PRATT, C, CAMPBELL, N, PAYNE, J AND REED, B (2000a) *Sustainable urban drainage systems – design manual for Scotland and Northern Ireland.* C521, CIRIA, London

MARTIN, P, TURNER, B, WADDINGTON, K, DELL, J, PRATT, C, CAMPBELL, N, PAYNE, J AND REED, B (2000b) *Sustainable urban drainage systems – design manual for England and Wales.* C522. CIRIA, London

MARTIN, P, TURNER, B, DELL, J, PAYNE, J, ELLIOTT, C AND REED, B (2001) *Sustainable urban drainage systems – best practice manual.* C523, CIRIA, London

NATIONAL SUDS WORKING GROUP (2003) "Framework for sustainable drainage systems (SUDS) in England and Wales". Consultation document, NSWG, Cheltenham

PRATT, C, WILSON, S and COOPER, P (2002) *Source control using constructed pervious surfaces. Hydraulic, structural and water quality performance issues.* C582, CIRIA, London

SAMUELS, P, WOODS-BALLARD, B, ELLIOTT, C, FELGATE, J AND MOBS, P (2004) *Sustainable water management in land use planning.* C630, CIRIA, London

SEPA, EA and EHS (2001) *Sustainable urban drainage systems – an introduction.* Scottish Environmental Protection Agency, Stirling; Environment Agency, Bristol; Environment and Heritage Service, Belfast

WILSON S, BRAY R and COOPER, P (2004) *Sustainable drainage systems. Hydraulic, structural and water quality advice.* C609, CIRIA, London

WRc (2001) *Sewers for adoption*, 5th edn. WRc, Swindon

USEFUL WEBSITES

CIRIA	http://www.ciria.org http://www.ciria.org/suds
Department for Environment, Food and Rural Affairs	http://www.defra.gov.uk/
Environment Agency	http://www.environment-agency.gov.uk
Office of the Deputy Prime Minister	http://www.odpm.gov.uk
Ofwat	http://www.ofwat.gov.uk